Marco Marker

He's a joker,
messing ab...
always mean...
if he sometim...
things wrong.

Philippa Feltpen

A real peacemaker, she helps keep the other Pens in order by sorting out arguments and giving good advice.

Splodge!
We're starting
school!

Waxy Max

He's very sporty and football mad. On the outside, he's tough, but underneath he's got the biggest heart.

Enter ...

Squiggle and Splodge

The Scribble twins! They're both quiet, both shy. Although they may not look alike, they do almost everything together.

Helping you to get
to know God more

Special Edition
Starting
School

Written by

Alexa
Tewkesbury

Squiggle and Splodge, the
youngest Pens characters,
discover that God is always
with them – even when they
begin the adventure of starting
school. A short story followed
by five days of Bible readings,
thoughts and prayers, based on
David and Goliath, to help young
children learn to trust in God.

What's inside?

Squiggle and Splodge were going to school – for the very first time.

Squiggle was excited.

She got out of bed early, washed her face and put on her brand-new school uniform. Then she went to find Splodge to show her how smart she looked.

But there was no sign of Splodge anywhere …

Suddenly, Squiggle spotted it.

A small bump under the bedclothes at the very end of Splodge's bed.

'I'm not sure,' mumbled Squiggle. 'I can't find Splodge – and there's something very odd in her bed!'

'Mmm,' Charlotte wondered thoughtfully. 'Have you prodded it?'

'Not yet,' replied Squiggle.

'I think you should,' Denzil said firmly. 'Right now.'

So Squiggle did.

'Ow!' cried the bump.

'You need to get up now, Splodge,' huffed Squiggle, 'or we'll be late for school.'

'I'm not going to school,' mumbled the bump, 'and I'm not getting up either. You'll have to manage without me.'

Charlotte sat down on the bed.

'Would it help,' she asked, 'if you knew your VERY BEST FRIEND was going to school with you?'

'I've got Squiggle going with me,' answered the bump, 'but I'm still nervous.'

9

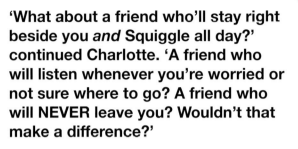

'What about a friend who'll stay right beside you *and* Squiggle all day?' continued Charlotte. 'A friend who will listen whenever you're worried or not sure where to go? A friend who will NEVER leave you? Wouldn't that make a difference?'

'I suppose,' murmured the bump. 'But who's going to do all that?'

'GOD,' beamed Charlotte. 'All you have to do is ask Him.'

The bump shuffled and squirmed and wriggled – and finally popped out from under the bedclothes.

'Promise?' Splodge said.

'I don't have to,' replied Charlotte. 'God's promised already.'

Splodge got out of bed. She put on her brand-new school uniform and looked in the mirror.

'I suppose,' she thought, 'I do look quite grown up.'

She picked up her brand-new school bag. It was blue with big white spots and a zip.

'I suppose,' she thought, 'I have got a brilliant bag to keep my things in.'

Inside the bag, her brand-new coloured crayons were tucked up in their brand-new stripy pencil case.

'I suppose,' she thought, 'starting school might not be SO scary if God's going there with me.'

Splodge looked worried.

'What about lunch?' she asked. 'I need lunch energy as well as breakfast energy. Where am I going to find lunch?'

'Everyone eats lunch together at school,' replied Philippa. 'You can take a packed lunch with you, or you can have a hot school meal.'

'Pudding, too?' Splodge asked hopefully.

'Pudding, too,' laughed Philippa. 'And you can take a drink and a snack with you for morning playtime.'

Gloria looked at the clock.

'Time to go,' she said.

'Oh dear …' mumbled Splodge.

'Don't worry,' smiled Squiggle. 'Remember what Charlotte said about our **VERY BEST FRIEND.**'

'Please, Lord God,' Splodge whispered, 'please stay with us all day.'

At the school gate Max and Marco were waiting.

16

The classroom looked big.

There were lots of chairs and tables.

There were books on shelves and colourful pictures on the walls … and coming towards them was a very TALL Pen.

17

Miss Fountain Pen led Squiggle and Splodge to a table where two more little Pens were already doing some colouring.

'This,' announced Miss Fountain Pen to Squiggle and Splodge, 'is Rowena Rollerball and Henry Highlighter.'

Rowena and Henry were very friendly. It was their first day at school, too.

'Did you think it was just you?' smiled Rowena.

Splodge nodded.

'Oh no,' said Henry. 'Lots of us are new today.'

They chattered together excitedly and Splodge began to feel much better.

How was your
first day?

At playtime, Squiggle and
Splodge and their new friends
ate their snacks together.

At lunchtime, they ate lunch
together in a big hall.

They explored their new school
together, too – and Miss
Fountain Pen taught them lots
of exciting, new things.

All too soon it was time to go
home again.

20

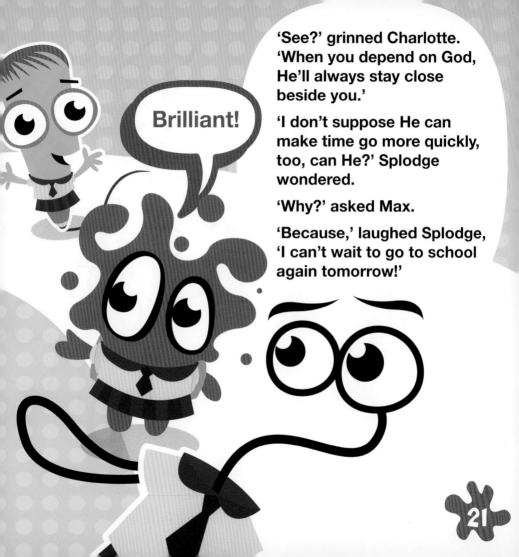

'See?' grinned Charlotte. 'When you depend on God, He'll always stay close beside you.'

'I don't suppose He can make time go more quickly, too, can He?' Splodge wondered.

'Why?' asked Max.

'Because,' laughed Splodge, 'I can't wait to go to school again tomorrow!'

Brilliant!

21

God's people, the Israelites, had some enemies.

One day, the Israelite army was camped on one side of a wide valley and the enemy army was camped on the other.

Suddenly, a HUGE man stepped out from the enemy camp. He was as big as a giant!

'Come on, you Israelites!' he roared across the valley. 'Choose one of your men to march over here and fight me. If he wins, we will come and work for you. But if *I* win, you will have to be our slaves!'

Starting school can sometimes seem scary – a bit like meeting a 'giant'!

If you feel nervous about your BIG DAY, who can you talk to?

Pens Prayer

Father God, thank You that every single day at my new school You will be there to listen when I need to talk to You. Amen.

David was an Israelite.

A small Israelite.

A young boy who looked after his father's sheep.

One day, David's father asked him to take some food to his brothers in the Israelite army. So David set off.

But just as he arrived, once again, Goliath stepped out of the enemy camp.

'Well?' he growled across the valley. 'Which one of you is going to come and fight me?'

David was only small when he met Goliath.

How tall are you? If you don't know, perhaps you could ask someone to measure you.

Pens Prayer

I thank You, dear Lord, that even though I feel very small and school seems very big, You are always with me. Amen.

The Israelite army heard Goliath's HUGE voice.

The Israelite army saw Goliath's ENORMOUS body.

And they were terrified.

But when small David heard Goliath's HUGE voice he decided, 'That's not right.'

When small David saw Goliath's ENORMOUS body he thought, 'How dare he frighten God's people?'

David wasn't scared at all. He knew God was with him.

You can trust God to stay close beside you at school, just as David trusted God to keep him safe.

Do you know any other stories about 'giants'?

Pens Prayer

Thank You, Father God, that whether I'm at school or at home or out and about, I can always trust in You completely. Amen.

David went to see the Israelite king.

'I'll fight Goliath for you,' he announced. 'I'm not afraid of him!'

The king raised his eyebrows.

'Have you seen the size of that giant?' he asked. 'You're so small. How could you possibly fight him?'

'With God beside me, I can face anything,' replied David. 'When I look after my father's sheep, sometimes lions and bears come after us. But God always saves me from them. I know he will help me fight Goliath.'

God ALWAYS helped David. He will ALWAYS help you, too.

If you have a problem or feel scared about something, what can you ask God to do?

Pens Prayer

Heavenly Father, thank You so much that You have promised to be with me WHEREVER I go. Amen.

David picked up his small sling and five small stones. When Goliath saw him, he roared with laughter. But, as ENORMOUS as Goliath was, God's power was BIGGER. It filled small David from head to toe.

Goliath marched towards him. David ran towards Goliath. As David got closer, he popped a stone into his sling. He whirled it round and round. Then –

WHAM! He hurled it towards Goliath.

WHACK! It hit Goliath on the head and down he fell!

With God's help, small David beat Goliath the giant – and the Israelite army cried, 'Praise the LORD!'

How do you feel about starting school? On your first day, remember how God filled David with His power!

 God's power is bigger than anything that may scare us!

Pens Prayer

Dear Lord God, I praise You because, just like David, I can be sure You will give me all the power I need every day. Amen.

Other Pens titles

Oooh! Look at all these exciting Pens books!

Each book contains 30 days of daily readings, stories, questions and prayers.